Purple Walrus

and

Other Perfect Pets

Contents

Purple Walrus

Written by John Parker   Illustrated by Fraser Williamson

Kate and Dad did not like Purple Walrus.
They wanted him to go away.

Dad was mad.
Purple Walrus was sad.
Purple Walrus went outside in the rain.
I went, too.

Purple Walrus played in the puddles.
He splashed and he splashed and he splashed.
He splashed a man and his dog.

The man was mad!

Purple Walrus was sad.
He sat down in the road.
The cars and the buses and the trucks stopped.
They honked their horns.

But Purple Walrus sat in the road.

A crane came and got Purple Walrus out of the way.

We sat in the rain and ate ice-cream cones.

It rained and it rained and it rained.
The man and his dog came back.

I looked at Purple Walrus and he looked at me.
We had a plan.

Purple Walrus took us across the road on his back.

When we got to the other side,
the man shook Purple Walrus's flipper.

Purple Walrus was happy.
I was happy, too.
We ran all the way home.

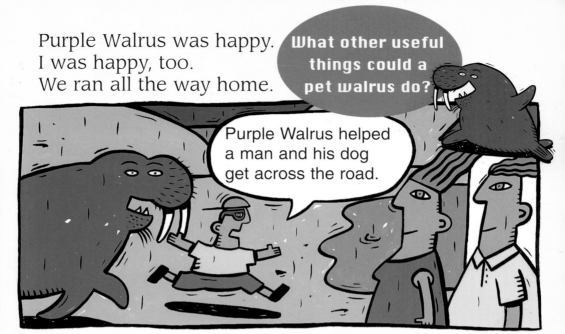

Dad and Kate were very happy.
They like Purple Walrus now.

Grandma's Cat

Written by Dot Meharry   *Illustrated by Linette Porter*

Mickey was Grandma's cat.
Mickey slept on Grandma's bed.
Mickey helped Grandma dig in the garden.
Mickey went shopping with Grandma.

Sometimes Grandma got Mickey something special,
like a nice cat toy or some fish.
Some days Mickey and Grandma sat in the sun.
They sat in Grandma's big, old rocking chair.
They rocked and they rocked and they rocked.

One day, all the family came to Grandma's house.
Grandma's children and grandchildren came.
Grandma's sister came, too.
She came in her shiny green car.
Her children and grandchildren came, too.
Grandma was very sick.
Everyone was sad.

That night Grandma died.
Dad said she had gone to be
with Grandad and Uncle Bill.
Everyone was very sad.
Everyone cried.

What special
thing did Mickey
like to eat?

11

The family stayed at Grandma's house
until the funeral was over.
The grandchildren looked for Grandma's cat.
They called and they called,
but they could not find Mickey.

When everyone had gone home,
Dad went to Grandma's house.
He called and called.
"Mickey, Mickey, Mickey.
Mickey, where are you?"
But Mickey never came.

Why do you think Dad couldn't find Mickey?

Every day Dad went to Grandma's house.
Every day he put food in Mickey's dish.
Every day he called, "Mickey, Mickey, where are you?
Mickey, Mickey, come out."
Every day the food was gone.
But Dad never saw Grandma's cat.

Soon Grandma's house was sold.
A great big dog was going to live there.
It didn't like cats.
Poor Dad.
He was so upset.
He went to Grandma's house.
"I'll just have to stay here
until Mickey comes out," he said.

Dad put Grandma's old rocking chair out in the sun.
He sat down in it.
He rocked and he rocked and he rocked.
The sun went down.

Dad woke up as the sun was coming up again.
He felt something soft and warm on his lap.
He could hear a purring sound.
Dad rocked the chair again and Mickey purred.

Why did Mickey come when Dad fell asleep in the chair?

Now Mickey lives with us.
He sleeps on Dad's bed.
He helps Dad dig in the garden.
He goes shopping with Dad.

Sometimes Dad gets Mickey something special,
like a nice cat toy or some fish.
Some days Mickey and Dad sit in the sun.
They sit in Grandma's big, old rocking chair.
They rock and they rock and they rock.

Yusof's Buffalo

Written by Marian Lough

Illustrated by Mrinal Mitra

Yusof had a buffalo.
The buffalo was called Itam.
Itam was a working buffalo.
Yusof loved Itam.

Yusof loved to go out and talk to Itam.
Itam would come up to the gate.
Yusof talked to Itam about a lot of things.
It was good to talk to Itam.

What are some things you know about buffalo?

16

One day Yusof saw a new red tractor by his house.
Yusof's father was standing by the tractor.
He was talking to a man.

The man was on the tractor.
He started the tractor.
All the time he was talking and talking.
"You can buy this tractor," said the man.
"You will like this tractor."

Yusof went inside.
"Is Dad going to buy a tractor?" he asked his mother.

"I think so," said Yusof's mother.
"What do you think of that?"

"It could be fun," said Yusof.
"I could learn to drive the tractor when I'm older."

But then Yusof said, "What about Itam?
Dad won't need Itam if he buys the tractor."

That night Dad said, "Do you like the tractor?"

"Yes, Dad," said Yusof, "but what about Itam?"

"I'll give him to Ali," said Dad.
"Itam is old.
Soon he will be too old to work."

Yusof was very sad.

When Yusof came home from school the next day,
the tractor was there.

Yusof went out to the gate.
He called out to Itam.
Itam came over.
"I think you know that I am sad," said Yusof.

What sorts of things will Yusof have to do to look after Itam?

That night Yusof's father said,
"I am going to buy the tractor.
What do you think, Yusof?"

Yusof said, "It's a very nice tractor, Dad,
but can we keep Itam?"

Yusof's father looked at Yusof's mother,
and she nodded.
"Yes, all right, Yusof.
You can keep Itam but you will have to look after him."

The man was right.
The tractor did the work fast.
Yusof's father was very happy with his new tractor.
Lots of people came to look at it.

Yusof went out to see Itam every day after school.
Yusof talked to Itam.
He told Itam that it was good that Itam was not at Ali's.

One night it rained and rained.
In the morning, Yusof's father went out on the tractor.

He was going down the path
when the tractor went down a hole.
The tractor stopped.
Yusof's father started the tractor again
but it was stuck in the mud.
It started to rain again.
Yusof's father did not want
his tractor to get wet.

What will
happen next?
What will Itam do?

Yusof's father ran back to the house.
"Yusof, go and get Itam," he said.

Yusof ran out and called Itam.
"Come on, Itam, we need you."

Yusof took Itam to the tractor.
Yusof's father tied a rope to the tractor.
He sat on the tractor.
"Now, Itam," he called, "Pull!"

Yusof stood by Itam and yelled, "Pull, Itam, pull!"

Itam pulled and pulled and pulled.

Yusof jumped up and down in front of Itam.

Yusof gave a big yell.
Itam gave a big pull.
Out came the tractor!

Yusof jumped up and down and gave Itam a big hug.

"Good boy, Itam.
I knew you could pull the tractor out!" Yusof said.

Yusof's father came over and gave Itam a pat.
"Good boy, Itam," he said.
"We need a buffalo and a tractor!"

Sam, the Seal Pup

Written by Jacqueline Crompton Ottaway

July 7

We saw a baby seal down at the beach today!
It was on the rocks.
The seal pup had big brown eyes.
It was very weak.
It had a big cut on its back flipper.
I went to pick it up.
Dad said we must not pick it up.
He said to keep
people and dogs away.
He went to call the seal rescue people.
A woman from the seal rescue place
came out to help the seal pup.
The woman said her name was Jess.
Jess said the pup was a week old.
She said it had cut its flipper on a boat motor.
Jess said maybe that is how the pup lost its mother.

Why should you never pick up a seal pup?

24

I called the seal pup Sam.
I wanted to take Sam home and look after him.
Jess said it was not a good idea.
Sam needed to have special food and medicine.
He needed to be with other seal pups.
Jess said she was going to take Sam
to the seal rescue place.
The seal rescue people will look after Sam.
Jess said we can call and find out
how he is doing.

July 9

We called the seal rescue place today.
They said that Sam is OK.
He is very thin, but he is being fed special food.
His special food is like real seal milk.
The cut on his flipper is getting better, too.

July 23

We called the seal rescue place again.
They said that Sam is better.
His flipper is better,
and he is in a little pool with other seal pups.
Jess is feeding him little fish.
He likes to swim in the pool
and sleep in the sun.

What do you think will happen next?

September 15

Jess sent us more photos of Sam today.
It doesn't look like Sam!
He is big and fat now.
Jess said he is eating fish all by himself.
He doesn't like people.
That is good, because Sam is a wild seal.
Jess said the seal rescue people
will take him back to the sea soon.
Jess said we can go and watch.
Dad says we can!

September 30

Jess met us at the beach.
She said to stay up on the rocks.
We looked at what was going on.
There were some wild seals
lying on the rocks in the bay.
The seal rescue people
took six big crates
down to the beach.
They opened the crates.
The seals came out of the crates.
They flopped down to the water.

What sorts of things does Jess have to know to do her job?

Sam was the last one.
The seals went into the water.
They swam in the bay.
They looked at the rocks and seaweed.
Then they swam out to the other seals.
I felt sad when Sam swam away,
but I am glad that he is going to be OK.

Remember

Never pick up a seal pup. Sometimes a pup is just resting on the rocks or shore while its mother hunts for food. You can best help a pup by watching from a distance. If the mother has not come back to the pup after four hours, call the police or the Fish and Wildlife Service for help.

The author and publisher wish to thank the Wolf Hollow Wildlife Rehabilitation Center for their generous help.

Glossary

🐾 **flippers** – flat limbs on animals (such as walruses, and seals) that are used for swimming

🐾 **funeral** – a ceremony held at a planned time and place for people to bury the dead

🐾 **rehabilitation** – the help given to sick or hurt animals (and people) to make them well again

🐾 **rocking chair** – a chair made with curved bars or springs fitted to the legs that people use for sitting and rocking in

🐾 **walrus** – a mammal, with thick skin and tusks, that can live on the land and in the sea

🐾 **working buffalo** – buffalo that are trained to pull the tools that help people grow crops and farm the land